Chris

To Jenny, Katie and Brian,
Merry Christmas to
all of you! Have Mommy
or Daddy read this
Story to you. I hope
you will be able to
enjoy it together.
My happiest wishes.
to you and your
Mother and Father.
From
Luke

AND IT CAME TO PASS

Bible Verses
and Carols
Selected by
Jean Slaughter
Illustrated by
Leonard Weisgard

The Macmillan Company, New York, New York

And it came to pass
in those days,
that there went out
a decree from
Caesar Augustus,
that all the world
should be taxed.
And Joseph also
went up unto the
city of David which
is called Bethlehem
with Mary his
espoused wife, being
great with child.

And so it was,
that, while they were
there, the days were
accomplished that
she should be delivered.
And she brought
forth her firstborn son,
and wrapped him in
swaddling clothes,
and laid him in a
manger; because there
was no room for them
in the inn.

And there were in the same country shepherds abiding in the field, keeping watch over their flock by night. And lo, the angel of the Lord came upon them and the glory of the Lord shone round about them; and they were sore afraid. And the angel said unto them, fear not; for behold, I bring you good tidings of great joy, which shall be to all people. For unto you is born this day in the city of David a Saviour, which is Christ the Lord. And this shall be a sign unto you. Ye shall find the babe wrapped in swaddling clothes, lying in a manger.

And suddenly there
was with the angel
a multitude of
the heavenly host
praising God, and
saying, Glory to God
in the highest, and
on earth peace,
good will
toward men.

And they came
with haste, and
found Mary,
and Joseph,
and the babe
lying in
a manger.

And when
they had seen it,
they made known
abroad the saying
which was told them
concerning the child.
And all they
that heard it wondered
at those things
which were told them
by the shepherds.

But Mary kept
all these things,
and pondered them
in her heart.

And the shepherds returned, glorifying and praising God for all the things that they had heard and seen, as it was told unto them.

To Didi

The Bible verses are from
Luke 2 : 1, 4-14, and 16-20.

The music was arranged for piano and
guitar by Patricia Slaughter.

The pictures are painted in full-color
tempera and the line drawings are done
in pen and ink on Japanese rice paper.
The type face is Palatino.